HUCKLEBERRY FINN

MARK TWAIN

Adapted by Dr. Marion Kimberly

HAWK BOOKS

© 1990 Ediciones B, S.A., Barcelona, Spain

This edition published by Hawk Books Limited,
309 Canalot, 222 Kensal Road, London W10 5BN

ISBN 0 948248 28 9

Printed in Spain

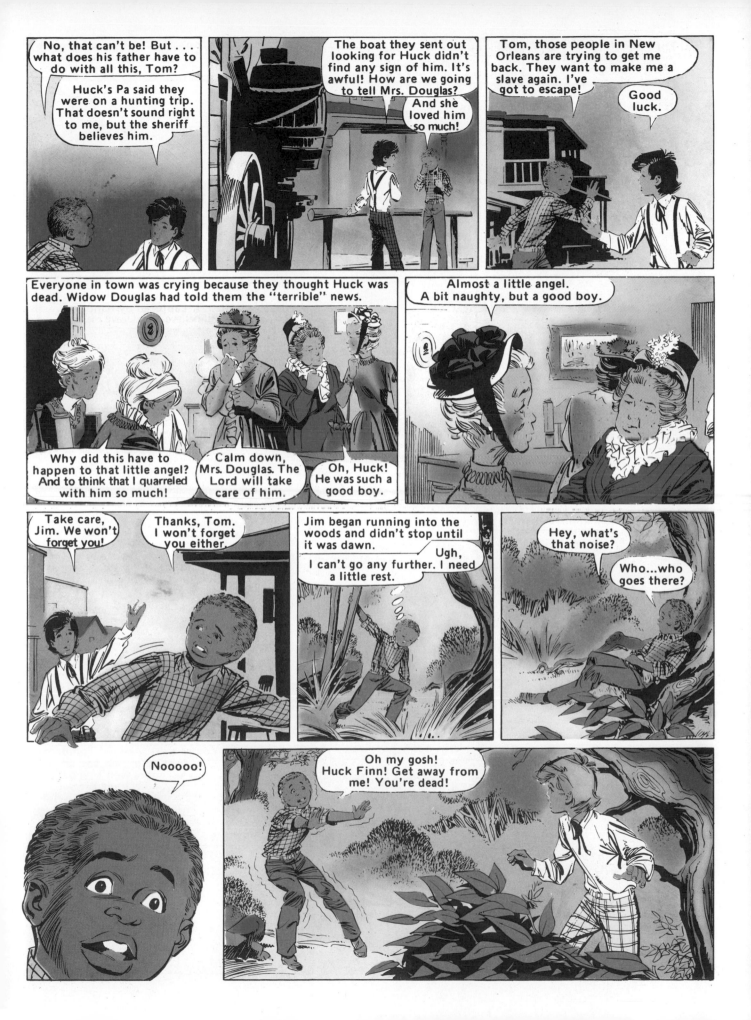

The boat's in good condition, but there's not much room.

Let's go!

Huck and Jim quickly left the boat that was aground . . .

Hurry up, row! If we don't, we're goners!

Meanwhile, in the town, people were growing more concerned about Huck's disappearance. His father told the sheriff...

You see, Sheriff, when I got back to the cabin, the boy wasn't there. I'm sure he was carried off by robbers.

Huck's father kept quiet about being drunk when Huck disappeared. And of course he didn't tell anyone that he really wanted to get Huck's money.

Do you believe the boy was killed?

Sheriff, I don't even want to think about that!

What were you and Huck doing in that cabin? Huck lives with Widow Douglas who adopted him.

The boy wanted to spend some time with me in the woods.

He also didn't mention that he had taken Huck from the Widow's house by force! Huck had been his prisoner in the cabin!

All right. But for now, I advise you not to leave town until we find out exactly what happened.

I won't, Sheriff...

Hmm, I don't like the direction this thing is taking. I think I'd better tone it down and forget about Huck's money.

Two days later, Huck and Jim pulled up to a pier . . .

Look, at least we've come as far as Illinois.

But I want to get to the northern part. In the north I can be a free citizen.

Over there all black men and women are free! If only I could get there I wouldn't have to fear my masters from New Orleans, or worry about being a slave again.

Later, as Huck prepared to go ashore . . .

You stay here. I'll go and see where we are. Don't let anyone see you. I'll be as quick as I can.